To Jamie, Alice, Lucia and Harry

For all children who have been to Rosslyn Chapel
and those who might come in the future.

William the Cat
and the Rescue of Rosslyn Chapel

Written by The Countess of Rosslyn
Illustrated by Rosie Wellesley

Once upon a time there was a cat called William.

He lived in the Scottish village of Roslin,
with the **Smith family**, who made
sure he always had a warm bed by the fire.

But William was no ordinary cat.
He had a very important job.

Every morning, after breakfast,
he left the house and walked through the village,
to the place where he spent his days.

You see William was
the **guardian** of

Rosslyn Chapel.

His father William had been guardian before him and his grandfather William before that.

Sometimes he heard the guides talking about 'a long line of Williams' looking after the Chapel, which made him very proud.

His main job was to take care of the **mice.**

There were plenty of cosy corners
where mice could make
their nests . . .

. . . but William was having none of it –

this Chapel was no
place for **mice!**

William had another important job too.
He kept an eye on everyone who lived in the Chapel.

Every morning, he let himself in . . .
. . . and went to say **hello** to his friends.

He always started with

Sir William St Clair.

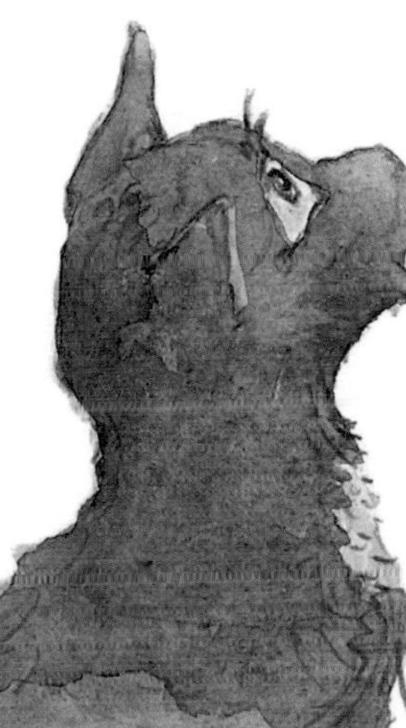

Sir William was a very important man, who built the Chapel over 500 years ago.

He looked a bit fierce, with a crown on his head and a sword in his hand, but he always exchanged a wink with William the Cat.

After this, William went to say a special hello to the **Elephant.**

He wanted to make him feel welcome in the Chapel, because he must have come a long way from his home.

There aren't many elephants living in Scotland are there?

In fact William was rather puzzled how there also came to be a **Lion**, a **Unicorn** and a **Camel** living there. But he didn't like to ask, just in case it sounded unfriendly.

Next he made his way to the **Apprentice Pillar**, the most important pillar in the Chapel.

At the base of the pillar lived the **Chapel Dragons,** who were his special friends. They watched over the Chapel at night and reported to William every morning.

Today, they told him to go and
see the Green Man.

William thought how clever it was that the Green Man had such a long neck, sticking out from the wall, to help him see everything that was going on.

Today, he was a bit concerned because he had spotted one of the Angels crying in the night.

The Angels were hidden high up above the pillars, looking down on the Chapel.

Each one had a different musical instrument:

a flute, a violin, a medieval pipe called a shawm . . .

and even some Scottish bagpipes.

They never played when anyone was listening, but sometimes, in the dead of night, when it was very windy, the Dragons heard them play their mysterious music.

This morning one of the Angels was in tears. She was worried about a large sad face high up in the corner, who had been suffering from the cold for a very long time.

During the night, it had been so cold and wet in the Chapel that part of his nose had finally crumbled . . .

. . . and fallen

right

off.

It was true. Rain was dripping through the roof and creeping in through the windows, making all the stone wet. Soon, other carvings might catch cold and start to crumble away too.

Then what would become of the beautiful Chapel?

William *shivered.*
It really was cold.

What had become of the heating pipes
under the floor that he used to love . . .
when there was actually warm air
coming out of them?

He looked at the poor face that
had lost his nose – and then at
all the other carvings.

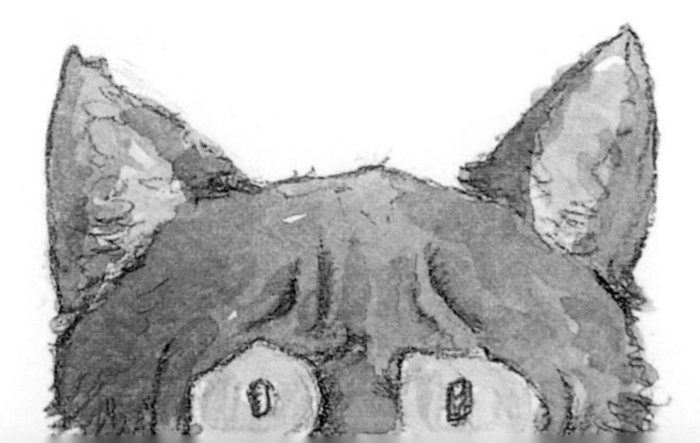

They looked cold and miserable too.

William was the guardian of this Chapel.
He knew what he had to do.

He **leapt up** onto the ledge and
made his way carefully along underneath
the windows,

trying hard not to look down . . .

Just as his paws were beginning to **wobble** . . .
in came a crowd of people to look round
the Chapel.

William took a deep breath
and let out a loud

meeeeeeeow!

They all looked up.

'Look at poor William – he's stuck!' they said.

The **guide** ran to get a ladder . . .

and two **children** stretched out a coat, so that William could jump onto it.

But William wanted them to see the poor sad face. He was the one who really needed help.

Feeling really **brave,** he raised his paw and pointed.

'Look at that face up there!' said a boy, 'He's lost his nose.'

William's job was done. He jumped down into the safety of the children's coat, where everyone made a very special fuss of him.

The next day, people came to examine the Chapel.

They said that the roof and windows were leaking and rain was damaging the stone.

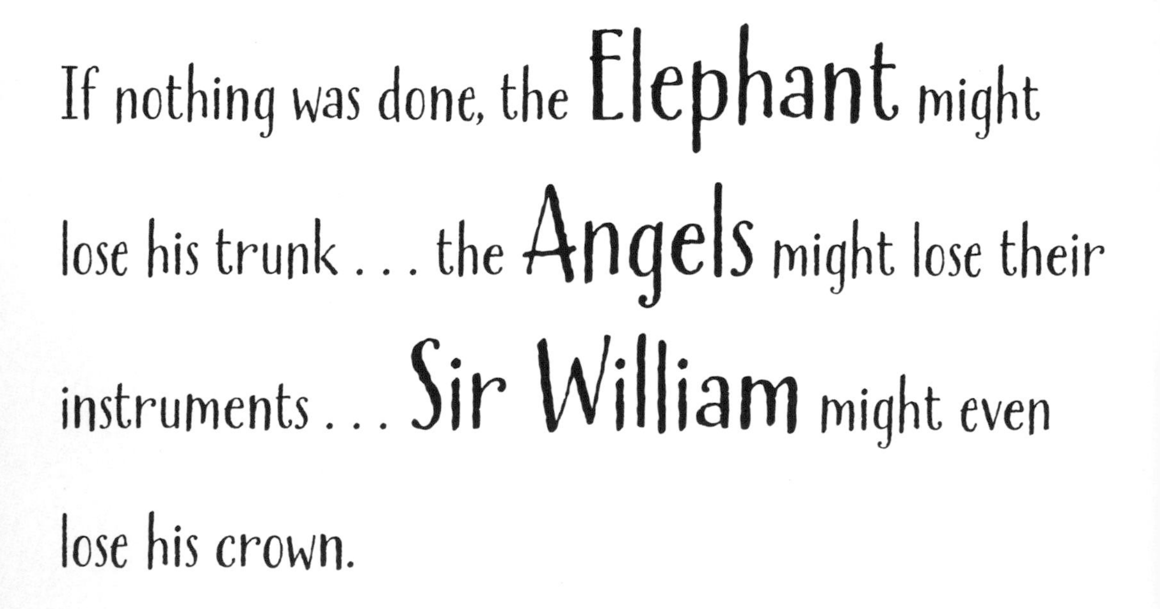

If nothing was done, the **Elephant** might lose his trunk . . . the **Angels** might lose their instruments . . . **Sir William** might even lose his crown.

So they all made plans for something called a

Conservation Project

To do:
1. Mend the roof
2. New windows
3. More heating

Which William could see meant lots of people in
bright yellow hats and jackets,
coming with tools and ladders to fix the Chapel.

They built a big **canopy** over the Chapel to protect it from the rain. They examined parts of the Chapel that hadn't been seen for ages.

They even discovered a **beehive** in one of the pinnacles, much to their surprise . . .

. . . and William's amusement.

They gave the Chapel a new lead roof,

they mended the leaky windows, and they

made it all windproof and watertight,

so that all the sad faces were warm

and dry and happy again.

But best of all, they put new heating pipes under the floor. . .

. . . with warm air coming out of them.

So I'm sure you can guess where William spends his days now.

I think he deserves it, don't you?

This book was conceived and underwritten by a generous grant from
Renee Harbers
and
The Harbers Family Foundation

All proceeds will support the ongoing conservation efforts of Rosslyn Chapel Trust
to preserve Rosslyn Chapel for future generations

Soli Deo Gloria

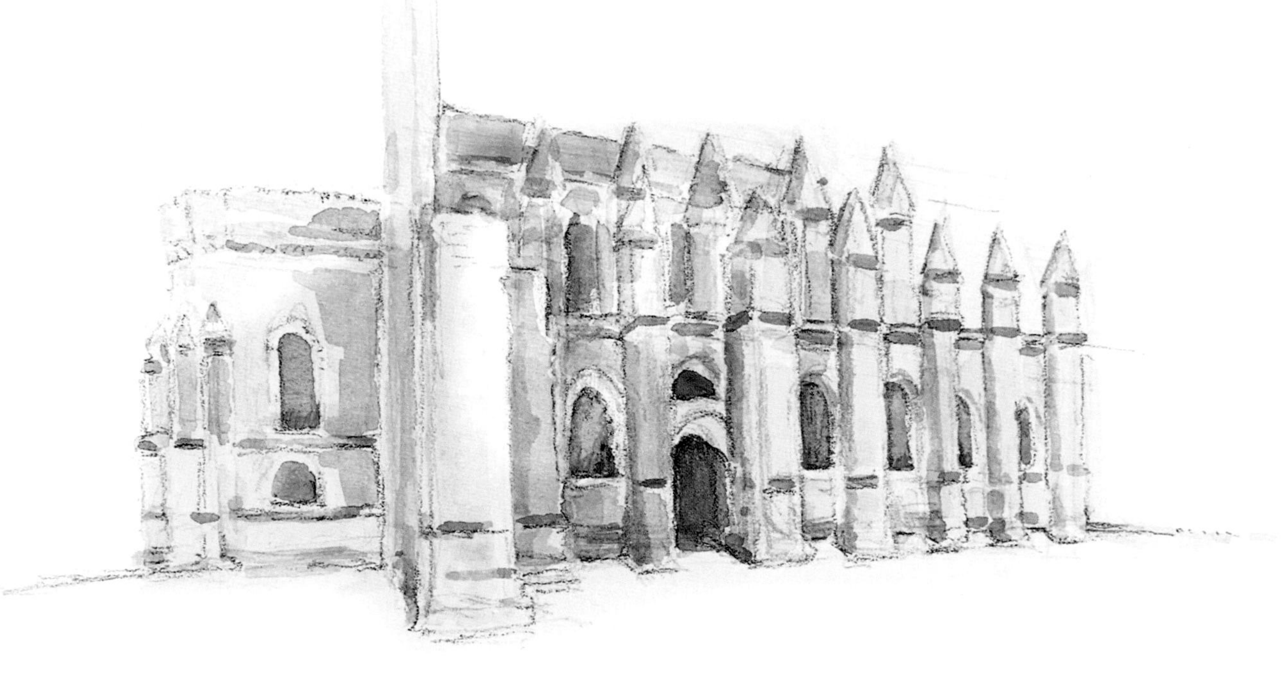

First published in 2015 by Rosslyn Chapel Trust

Design by Studioarc

Printed in Scotland by J Thomson Colour Printers using FSC certified paper

Thanks to Matthew and Kate Smith for sharing William the Cat with Rosslyn Chapel's visitors